COSMIC GIRLS

WRITTEN BY: MANUEL GODOY
ILLUSTRATED BY: JOSHUA BULLOCK

THE YEAR IS 2255

I AM A HUNTER OF THE GALACTIC EMPIRE OF EARTH

TODAY, WE HUNT PIRATES

INFILTRATION COMPLET

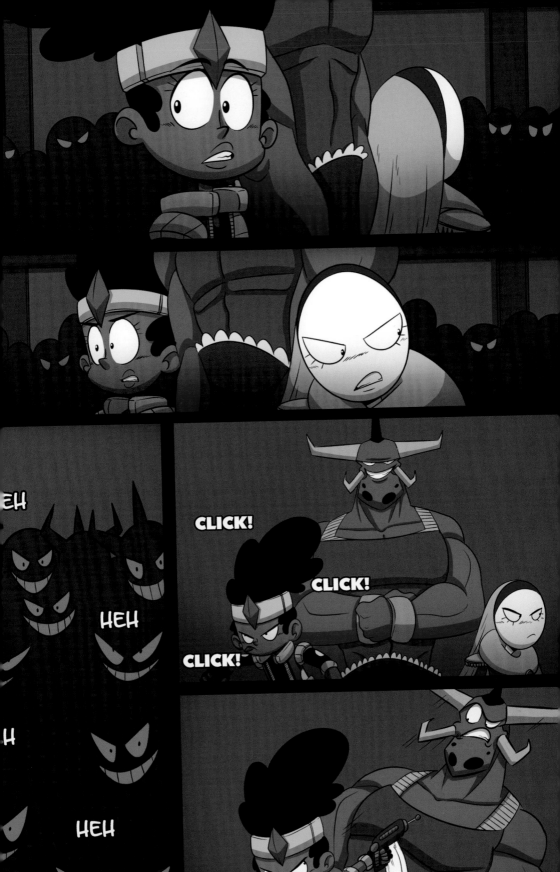

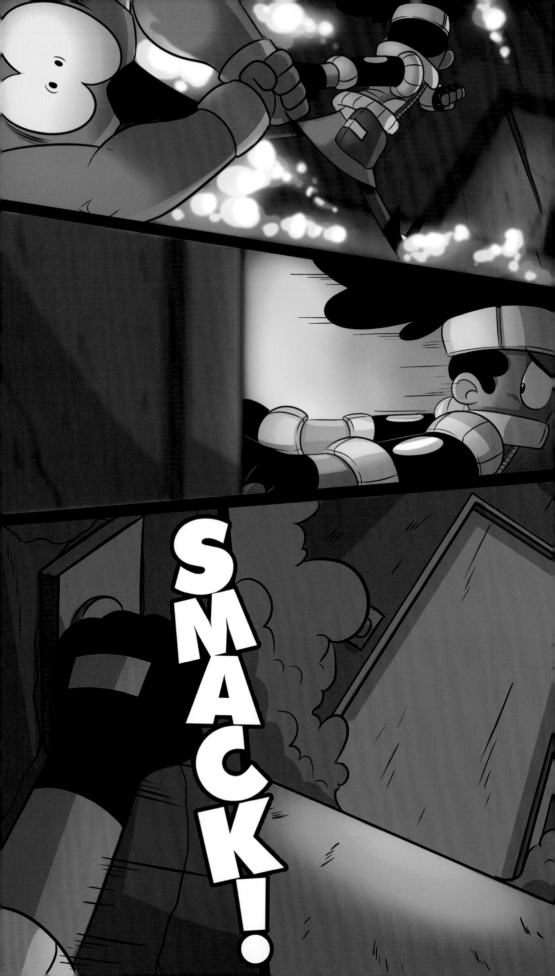

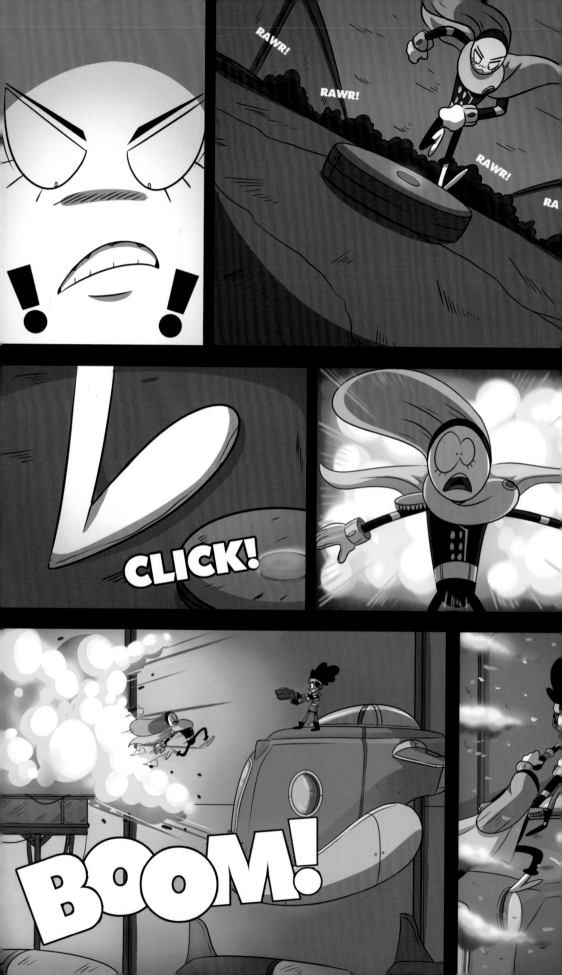

GET THE BIG GUN NOW!

HH!

HUFF

PUFF

SHOOOM

BOOM

CLICK!

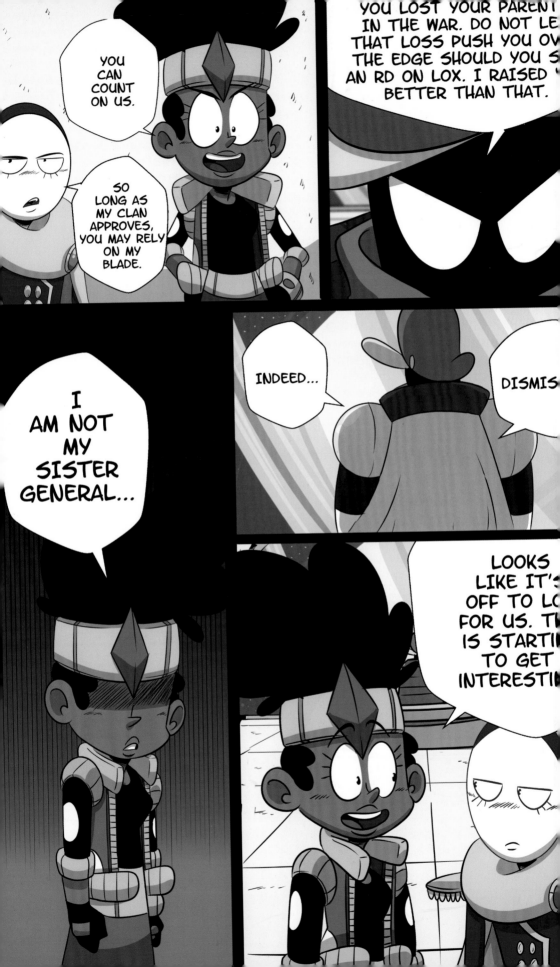

THANKS FOR READING!

CORINA

DURASI

WRITER / DIRECTOR
MANUEL
GODOY

ARTIST
JOSHUA
BULLOCK

WANT TO BE A PART OF BLACK SANDS?

CONTACT MANUEL GODOY FOR INVESTMENT OPPORTUNITIES.
WE ARE ALWAYS LOOKING FOR PATRONS AS WE STRIVE
EVER FURTHER.

EMAIL: mgodoy@blacksandsentertainment.com

 **@blacksandsentertainment**

Official Store: Blacksandsentertainment.com

 www.patreon.com/blacksands

IF YOU LOVE SCIENCE FICTION ADVENTURES, YOU WILL LOVE COSMIC GIRLS!

COSMIC GIRLS FOLLOWS THE JOURNEY OF CORINA, A THIRTEEN-YEAR OLD WAR ORPHAN WHO BECOMES A BOUNTY HUNTER FOR THE UNITE EMPIRE OF EARTH IN A DISTANT FUTURE. SHE IS AMAZING AT HER JOB BUT HER IMMATURITY CAN SHOW UP AT THE WORST OF TIMES. SHE IS ACCOMPANIED BY AN ALIEN COMPANION NAMED DURASI, WHO COMES A STRONG LINE OF WARRIORS. THESE TWO TAKE ON THE GALAXY'S MC NOTORIOUS VILLAINS IN A COMPLICATED SETTING WHERE TWO MAJC EMPIRES ARE VYING FOR POWER OVER THE GALAXY.

WRITTEN BY THE FAMED WRITER OF BLACK SANDS, MANUEL GODOY

ISBN 978-1-73396

BLACK SANDS
ENTERTAINMENT

9 781733 960915